MOLLY and BABOU

James Mahoney and Marie-Paule Mahoney

of

Mahoney

AuthorHouse™
1663 Liberty Drive
Bloomington, IN 47403
www.authorhouse.com
Phone: 1-800-839-8640

Published by AuthorHouse 6/19/2014

ISBN: 978-1-4969-1851-2 (sc)
ISBN: 978-1-4969-1852-9 (e)

Library of Congress Control Number: 2014910550

Any animals depicted in stock imagery provided by Thinkstock are models,
and such images are being used for illustrative purposes only.
Certain stock imagery © Thinkstock.

This book is printed on acid-free paper.

authorHOUSE®

Dedicated to Molly, Rags, and Pupsie, our deeply loved canine
friends who enriched our lives in so many ways

Front cover painting and design and paintings pages 3, 31, 37, 41, 56, 97:
Gosha Karpowicz
www.FineArtsandYoga.com

Table of Contents

Chapter One

A Voice in the Forest

Molly crossed the wooden bridge over the little stream and entered the forest. She sometimes liked to be alone first thing in the morning, away from Rags and Pupsie, her adopted sisters. It wasn't that she didn't love them or care about them. It was more the strain of feeling responsible for them all the time, having to tell them what they must do or could not do. Now she was free—at least for a while.

With her nose to the ground, she zigzagged along the foot-worn trail. She was trying to pick up the scents of animals.

She had not gone far when a distant, gruff voice called out from high up in the dense trees ahead.

"Hello!" it said.

"Who's there?" Molly answered as she came to a sharp halt. Her ears drew back in sudden fear, her body began to tremble, and her heartbeat raced in terror.

She searched the branches against the glare of the bright-blue sky. At first, she could not make out precisely where the voice had come from. Then Molly's eye picked out an enormous black, hairy mass that seemed to hang from the branches. She wished she could glide through the air and make a beeline for home and the safety of her mama's embrace. But, paralyzed by fear, she was unable to move.

"Who's there?" she repeated.

"I am a bear, can't you see?"

"I meant, what do you want?" Molly said, her voice shaky and her legs wobbly.

"To speak with you."

"Why?"

"Because I am lonely," the bear replied, "so very lonely."

"What is your name?" Molly asked as she finally regained control.

"My what?" he said, sounding a little confused.

Just as Molly was about to answer him, a shrill voice broke the silence of the forest.

"Molly, M-o-l-l-yyyyy … where's my Mol?"

"Did you hear that?" Molly asked as she pricked up her ears.

"Yes, what was it?"

"That was my mama calling me. I have to go home right away."

"But why?" the bear said in surprise.

"Because she worries if I stay away in the forest too long."

The bear seemed perplexed by this. "Please, come back and see me tomorrow," he said.

There was a long silence before Molly gathered the courage to ask the bear, "Why?"

"Because I would like to be your friend."

What a nice thing to say, Molly thought.

"I often see you exploring the woods with your two friends and I think, that must be nice to have close friends like that."

"They are my stepsisters," Molly replied.

After a pause, she added, "All right, I shall come to visit you tomorrow, if you promise me you will not cross the bridge and step onto our land. You must also promise to stay *much* further back in the woods. My younger sister, Pupsie, will become very frightened if she finds your scent on our land."

"I promise," the bear said.

"And stay higher up in the trees, as well," Molly added for good measure.

"I will, I will," the bear said resolutely.

"Well, you have my word."

As Molly turned to rush back home, a sudden gust of wind swirled the autumn leaves high into the sky. They seemed to chase the flittering little birds. She could not see their magnificent reds and golds, because like all dogs, she saw the world only in black, white, and gray. Besides, she was blind in one eye and poor-sighted in the other. One would never have guessed, watching her run through the forest. She could skip across fallen tree trunks and spring over bushes with the accuracy and grace of a deer in flight.

As she entered the house, Molly wondered why she had made such a promise, and to a bear of all creatures.

Chapter Two

Dogs and Deer

Early the next morning, Molly, Rags, and Pupsie rushed out of the house to investigate who had been on their land during the night. They were as tight as any pack of wild dogs roving the African plains, and they loved to pretend that they were out on hunting forays. It made them feel important.

Instantly, the squirrels returned to the safety of their nests in the treetops. Running for their lives, the chipmunks reached their hidden burrows beneath the stone walls.

Deer having fun on the land

Unexpectedly, five white-tailed deer appeared on the dogs' land.

"Who do they think they are, invading our land like this?" Rags complained to Molly and Pupsie. She let out a bloodcurdling war cry.

"Let's show them who we are!"In a silent sort of dog Morse code, she gave commands and sideway glances back and forth to alert Molly and Pupsie of her plan of attack. The dogs raced the deer back and forth across their land and their neighbor's land. Suddenly, the deer turned and chased the dogs back, jumping in huge loops through the air. They soon became exhausted and dropped out of the chase. The deer returned to the woods, except for one of the twins, who seemed to want to interact with the three dogs in a friendly way.

"Let's hide in the bush," Molly yelped to Pupsie and Rags. Her heart felt like it was going to explode at any moment from the effort of her running. The deer tiptoed next to the bush, and her nostrils twitched, a sure sign that she had picked up on a wisp of dog's scent. "She's trying to play hide and seek," Molly whispered. The dogs held their breath until the deer passed their hiding place. Tired of the game, she disappeared into the woods.

The dogs returned to their tasks of checking hidden smells. The three of them shared a genuine closeness and attachment for each other, despite their differences in personality and occasional misunderstandings.

Molly was a pretty little dog, seven years of age, very intelligent but sometimes a tiny bit arrogant. Bossy at times, she was the leader and the thinker of the trio.

Pupsie and Rags

Rags, a four-year-old sheepdog, had the marking of a Border collie, but with a chestnut and white coloration. She was a frolicking, happy soul with her hair always in a mess. She had a very sweet nature, although at times, she would have little tizzy fits. On one such occasion, she pulled a bouquet of roses that dada had bought for mama to pieces with her claws.

At three years of age, Pupsie, or Pups as she was often called, was still a puppy at heart. She was brindle-colored. The peacemaker of the group, she was ready at a moment's notice to step in and calm Rags's first muffled growls to say that she had had enough of Molly's petty rules. Molly controlled where each of them was allowed to stand and eat their "din-din." Molly's strictest rule was that she was the only one who could lie next to Mama in bed at night.

Rags soon got bored of smelling the plants and went back home. No doubt, she was hoping to get an extra after-breakfast treat from mama, now that she would be alone in the house. Pupsie followed, not wanting to miss out on what Rags might get.

Thank goodness, Molly thought.

She waited a short while, just to make sure she really was alone, and then turned and raced across the bridge. Guided by her sensitive nose, she followed the winding trail through the forest in a side-to-side fashion. The bear must have kept to his promise and stayed deeper in the woods, because she could find no trace of his smell at first. Then the bear shouted out in his husky voice, "What's a name?"

Molly stared up into the dense canopy of trees and saw the bear's huge, black mass high up among the branches.

"A name is what mamas and dadas give to call us when we are born."

The bear scratched the side of his head with his huge front paw and thought for a while. "I guess I don't have a name," he finally concluded with obvious disappointment. "Nobody ever calls me."

Molly sensed that the bear was deeply lonely. Feeling his sadness, she blurted out, "I'll give you one."

Like a wolf, she raised her head toward the sky and started to utter a high-pitched howl, followed by a softer, drawn-out yowl. The bear mumbled along in imitation, with great pleasure.

"Baaa-bou," Molly howled.

"Baaa-bou!" he repeated in his deep, coarse voice. "I like the sound of that."

"Your mama called you 'Molly' yesterday. That's a very pretty name."

"Yes, I like it. My mama and dada gave me the same name as my real mother."

"Why?"

"Because I was the only one of my seven brothers and sisters who looked like her."

"Seven brothers and sisters! Wow! That's a lot," Babou said with surprise. "I know that mama bears often have twins, and sometimes even triplets, Molly, but I have never heard of eight cubs being born all in one go."

Babou started to slowly make his way down the tree, paw by paw, his enormous weight snapping branches and twigs as he went. He was even bigger than Molly had at first thought. Yet, for all his hugeness, she felt there was something gentle and soft about this giant. She sensed that he would never hurt her and, if anything, he would always protect her from harm.

"I must go home now, or mama will wonder where I am."

"Will you come and see me again tomorrow?" Babou asked.

"Yes," Molly promised, this time with no fear in her voice.

Chapter Three

Molly's Birth Place

Molly rushed to the door to be let out, first thing the following morning. To her surprise, neither Rags nor Pupsie followed. As she crossed the bridge, she started to hear a loud noise, which frightened her. It grew louder with every step that she took. She had never heard a sound quite like it before. *What could it possibly be?* she wondered, and she began to get alarmed. *Could it be some big, angry animal that could eat me?*

She need not have worried. It was only Babou stretched out on his back at the foot of a gnarled, old oak tree. His back legs paddled the air in circles, as if he were riding a bicycle upside down. His mouth was half open. He was in deep sleep, snoring like an old steam engine. He reminded Molly of her dada when he awakens everybody in the middle of the night with his snoring.

Babou suddenly woke up. "Oh! I'm so sorry, Molly." He blinked a few times and struggled to get to his feet. "I ate so many crabapples earlier this morning. Then I dropped by a garbage dump and discovered all sorts of goodies to eat. I was so full that I had to lie down and take a rest. I guess I must have fallen asleep." He rubbed his tummy in circles with his paw and licked his lips. "It was so good."

Food from a garbage dump! Molly was too horrified to ask him what he had eaten.

Sticking his tongue out, Babou added, "I am always hungry."

His tongue reminded her of an enormous chunk of strawberry ice cream, the sort that Rags loved so much to lick.

"Let me climb back up the tree," Babou said in a flustered voice. He didn't want to frighten Molly. He scrabbled to his haunches, reached up for the lowest branch, and began to pull himself up.

"No, Babou, there is no need to do that. Stay where you are. Tell me, where is your home?"

He thought for a while and then said, "I spend the winters in the mountains up north, and in the spring, I make my way here."

After a long pause, he added, "And you, Molly, where do you come from?"

Jamaican villagers get ready to go fishing

12

"My dada and my mama said that I was born on an island called Jamaica, which is surrounded by a big sea. Beautiful flowers dance in the wind all year round, and fruit trees grow everywhere. Men go out to fish every morning to feed their families."

"Whoa! Whoa!" Babou interrupted her excitedly. "Maybe I should go there. I would never be hungry again."

"Oh, but it is far, far away, and you would have to cross the sea to get there."

"I can swim, you know," Babou stated, a little offended by Molly's doubting remark. "Of course, maybe not as well as you. It must have taken you many days to reach land."

Molly was flattered by Babou's compliment. She pondered a while before telling him the truth. "I don't know whether I can swim or not, but I hate water."

"You do?" Babou said in total amazement.

"Especially when I get a bath," she added quickly. "The whole family stands around to gawk at me and says things like, 'Molly is so good!' or 'she is going to look so beautiful!'"

"Still, it must be nice to have people say things like that to you," Babou said.

"Not when I am squashed in the bathtub," Molly responded. "I don't like to be splashed with water and have soap rubbed into my hair. It's humiliating. I take such pride to groom myself thoroughly every day."

Babou seemed mystified. "So, how did you get here, then?"

"My mama and dada took me in an airplane."

"What is that?" Babou asked.

"It's like a gigantic, noisy bird, with large wings, a pointed nose, and a long tail. It lifts you off the ground and soars into the clouds and carries you wherever you want to go."

Babou thought for a while.

"I often hear them. They sometimes leave great, white lines in the sky."

Molly wasn't too sure what Babou meant by that.

"But why did your mama and dada bring you here?"

"It's a long story," Molly answered. "I'll tell you more tomorrow. I must go back home now."

Chapter Four

A Bond of Blood

Babou shook the branches of the old oak tree that had become his refuge. He had seen Molly coming through the woods. "Good morning, Molly. Can you finish your story?"

"Yes," she answered, happy that Babou had remembered.

She had heard her story so many times because she loves to stretch out under the kitchen table to listen to mama and dada telling it to people. She knew the details by heart.

"My father was called Shaba, a real African name, because he looked like the biscuit-colored Bush dogs of West Africa who roam the land. He was the top-ranking male in the whole of Treasure Beach, the little village in Jamaica where I was born. None of the other dogs ever dared to challenge him."

"What about your mother?"

"My mother was highly intelligent and genteel. She had a high position among all the dogs in the village."

"Why?" asked Babou.

Molly stopped a second to catch her breath. "You won't believe this, but further down the winding road from where we lived was a small restaurant called Jake's. Every evening, before the customers came, the chef would prepare a special dish just for my mother, 'because she was always such a wonderful dog.'"

Babou chuckled in his bear-like way. "Your mama was really lucky! But what about you, Molly?"

The house where Molly was born

"Well, my mother gave birth to my seven brothers and sisters under the foundations of a little, white wooden house—all in one go. The next day, she unexpectedly found herself squatting in pain again. As she stretched out on the sandy ground beneath the house, her tummy gave a sudden great heave—and out popped another puppy."

"It was you, Molly?" Babou said, all excited.

"Yes! I was what is known as a runt puppy. I was very sickly and only half the size of my siblings. The lids of both my eyes were matted together with pus. Later, it turned out that one of my eyes would burst, and I lost part of my vision. The sight in my other eye wasn't good either. I also had difficulty breathing because I had pneumonia. My brothers and sisters would knock me over every time I tried to get to my mother's nipples to nurse."

Molly's mother with her puppies

"But why would they bully you, Molly?"

"Because my legs were so weak and wobbly, I could not to stand up to them."

"That must have been horrible! how did you manage to survive?" Babou asked.

"I was lucky. In the house next to ours, a man and his wife had come to spend their vacation. The man was a vet and—"

"A vet, what is that?" Babou interrupted.

"A veterinarian, a doctor who fixes animals when they are ill, like doctors do for sick people."

"I did not know there were such people!"

That's a strange thing for Babou to say, Molly thought.

Molly seeking the security of dada's tennis shoes

"He realized that I was in bad shape, with many things wrong with me. He was most concerned about my blood." Then, Molly could not resist saying, in a condescending sort of way, "You probably do not know what blood is, do you?"

"Yes, I do," he replied immediately. "One day, I was drinking from a stream in the forest when I heard people scream, 'there he is! there he is! I see him! I see him!' At that very moment, something sharp pierced the skin of my back and I heard a loud bang. The pain was terrible, but I managed to stagger away and reach the top of a steep hill covered in trees. There, I collapsed and passed out. When I woke up the next morning, I could not believe my eyes. My coat was covered in a thick, sticky, dark-colored liquid."

"It was blood?" Molly interrupted.

"Yes!" Babou said, nodding his head several times.

Molly stared at Babou in silence. She felt so guilty for her snappy comment about his not knowing what blood was, and she was deeply touched by his story. "You were so courageous, Babou. Nothing like that ever happened to me. My blood was sick, that was all. My dada often tells people, 'Molly had severe anemia when she was a puppy.'"

"It must have been difficult to make your blood become thick and normal again," Babou said.

"I'd say so," she replied. "The vet took some good blood from one of my mother's front legs with a big, long thing called a syringe and needle. Then, he gave it to me into a vein in my tummy."

"Did it hurt?"

"I don't remember; I was only four weeks old at the time. The vet told his wife that I had so many problems that they would have to take me home with them to America or I would die. So they did. I nearly died five times before I was three years old, but since then, I have been very strong and healthy."

"So the vet and his wife became your dada and mama," Babou said.

"Yes! Those are the names their three children call them by."

Molly realized that both she and Babou must have come close to death. Unlike Molly, Babou had recovered all on his own, without any help from anyone else. From then on, Babou never had to ask her to come back and see him. They had bonded, there and then. They were friends.

Chapter Five

Of Berries and Foxes

Hardly a cloud flecked the sky as Molly crossed the humpbacked bridge to enter the woods. She could see Babou far off in the distance, standing upright under his huge oak tree. He looked so tall and regal, a real giant of the forest.

"How would you like me to take you for a ride in the forest this morning?" he called out

"A ride in the forest?" what was Babou talking about, she wondered? It was one

thing when Dada asked her and her sisters if they wanted to go for a ride around the ponds in the village, but that was in the car.

"How could we go for a ride in the woods, Babou?"

"Simple!" he replied. "Climb on my back and I will show you."

"It sounds very dangerous to me," Molly responded. "I could fall and hit my head on the ground."

"No! I will not let you fall."

Babou bent down on all fours. Very cautiously, Molly climbed onto his back. "You can dig your claws into my fur and even dig them into my skin if you feel frightened that you will fall." And off they set.

At first, Molly kept her head down, buried deep in Babou's soft, wiry coat. She was too afraid to look up to see where they were going. She could hear his heart pounding in his chest. She dug her claws into his tough skin to hold on tighter. He did not complain.

After a while, she began to relax. The warmth of his back made her feel secure. Finally, she raised her head. Everything looked so wonderfully different from high above the ground. Like all dogs, Molly had a sense of smell that was one thousand times more sensitive than a human being's. The flowers and leaves of the wild columbine, vanilla, and May apple bushes had marvelous scents that she had never experienced before. The wind sang in her ears and blew through her fur. She felt invigorated.

Babou turned his head to look back at her. "How are you feeling, Molly?"

"Fine," she shouted back as she felt more and more relaxed.

"I knew you would like it. Wait till you see the berries. You'll love them. They are scrumptious," Babou said, licking his lips in ecstasy.

Within no time at all, they reached a huge tangle of bushes covered in round, purplish elderberries. "Hang on, Molly!" Babou called out. Standing on his hind legs, he grabbed great bunches of berries with his claws.

"Here, Molly," he said, offering her some. "Try these. They are my favorite berries." He was obviously pleased with himself. A big, happy smile spread across his face.

"Thank you so much, but I cannot eat them," Molly replied sadly.

"You can't?" Babou said in amazement. "But why not?"

"Fruits make me ill. As my dada often tells people, 'Molly is still very fragile and we have to be careful what we give her to eat.'" This time, Babou understood her point.

From one paw to the other, back and forth, he scraped the berries from his claws with his teeth and tongue, grunting in happiness as he gorged himself. "I am full, Molly. My stomach is going to burst. I'm sorry you couldn't eat the berries. They were so good!" With his regained energy, he added, "I should take you home, or your mama will start to worry. We have been away for quite a while."

"Yes," said Molly, "but it has been fun."

Off they set for home. They had hardly gone any distance when suddenly Babou stuck his forelegs out in front of him and, using them like powerful brakes, brought himself to an instant stop. A dog-like creature stood in the middle of the trail in front of them. He reminded Molly of Rags, with his caramel-colored coat and his long, bushy tail with a black tip.

The arrogant fox

"Hello, Fox," said Babou. "Long time since I have seen you."

"Hello, Mr. Bear," the fox replied with obvious respect. His ears erect, he scrutinized Molly intently. "What do you carry on your back?"

Molly did not like the tone of the fox's voice, and the hackles on the back of her neck spiked immediately.

"This is Molly," Babou responded, then added, "my friend, Molly. We went to search for berries."

The fox had always seen the bear alone, and he seemed surprised and a little put out by Molly's presence. "I am searching for chickens to eat," he said.

"Well, you won't find any around here," Molly replied with sarcasm in her voice.

He gave her a look of contempt, as if to say, "how would *you* know?"

Molly returned his stare without a blink. He yapped a few times, turned on his tail, and took off like a rocket in the opposite direction.

Chapter Six

Behind Lace Curtains

As Babou slowly gathered speed, they came upon a small group of deer grazing in a grassy knoll. To Molly's surprise, the deer did not show any fear at Babou's sudden appearance among them. They raised their heads to gaze at Molly and then at Babou for a moment before returning to their munching. Babou continued on his way, when Molly suddenly barked for him to stop. He executed his sudden-brake maneuver and came to a halt.

"Look at that strange cat ahead!"

"That is not a cat," he whispered. "That's Mrs. Raccoon."

Mrs. Raccoon

Molly had never seen an animal quite like this before. Her back was arched. She had long whiskers like a cat's, small, pointed ears, and dark-brown rings around her tail. Her most striking feature was her face. It had a broad, black band running from one cheek to the other and soft, brown eyes surveying the world around her.

"Hello, Mrs. Raccoon," Babou said. "Why are you all alone? where are your babies?"

"They are all grown up now and have gone on their way, Mr. Bear." She must have seen Molly on his back but seemed oblivious to her presence.

"What is the matter? you look so sad!" Babou said.

"Yes, I am very sad, Mr. Bear."

"But why?"

"Because of the way people treat me."

"What do you mean?"

"Well, when they first came here from the city and built their houses, they liked me and would call their children to come and look at me. Sometimes, they would even leave me treats to eat."

"What a nice thing to do," said Babou. "I have never got a treat from anybody."

Molly thought of all the treats she and her sisters receive.

"But everything has changed now," continued the raccoon.

"In what way?" asked Babou.

"I don't know why, but when they see me coming now, they have fear in their eyes. They call their children back into their houses and shout, 'Don't touch the raccoon, it might be dangerous!' or, 'Be careful that the raccoon doesn't bite you!' They stare out from behind their lace curtains and watch to see whether I am still there. Do you think there is something wrong with the way I look?" the raccoon lamented.

Babou bent down to sniff the raccoon thoroughly from nose to tail. Being closer now, Molly could not help but notice how elegant the raccoon's paws were. She had long, delicate fingers not unlike her mama's.

"I don't think there is anything wrong with you, Mrs. Raccoon," Babou finally said.

"Perhaps I am ugly," she responded.

"No, no, Mrs. Raccoon, not at all! I like the way you look." Molly wanted to add that she did, too, but she decided not to interfere in case she offended the raccoon.

"Then, Mr. Bear, why do people treat me that way?"

"I do not know."

"What hurts me the most is the look of disgust in their eyes. Is there something I have that makes them scared of me?"

"Like what, Mrs. Raccoon?"

"Like something that humans are afraid to catch from me, something that might make them ill."

I'm sure dada would know what Mrs. Raccoon is talking about, Molly thought. "I do not have an answer for you, Mrs. Raccoon," Babou said, "but I know how you must feel."

"But you are the king of the forest, Mr. Bear. How would you know how I feel?"

"A king in hiding," Babou replied sadly.

The raccoon uttered a plaintive little musical *orr-orr-orr* sound before turning and slowly waddling away. Babou remained thoughtful.

Molly was puzzled. *What is a king?* she wondered, *and why did Babou call himself a "king in hiding?"*

He knew so many things about nature and the animals of the forest that were all mysteries to her.

Chapter Seven

Molly's Secret

Babou must have sensed Molly's coming because he started to bounce up and down around the base of the old oak tree.

"Let's go," he said cheerily. "Your bark is my command."

"All right!" Molly replied with equal lightheartedness. She jumped on Babou's back, placed her forelegs around his neck, and held on as tightly as she could to his sides with her back paws.

"Ready, steady, go!" Molly yelled.

Babou shot off, and the autumn leaves piled on the ground blew all over them. In no time at all, Babou had broken into a sprint, dashing through the woods.

"Where are we going today?" Molly called out to him.

"Wait and see," he shouted back at her.

At that very moment, Molly heard a faint rumbling coming from far above their heads. She looked up and saw ragged, gray clouds scudding across the sky. The noise became louder, and she suddenly recognized it for what it was.

"Babou, please take me home right now."

"What's the matter, Molly?" he said with concern.

"You don't hear that roaring sound?"

"Yes, it comes from the sky, but it's nothing to worry about."

"It is called thunder, Babou. It comes when the sky is angry and tells the people that she is mad with them. When she gets really enraged, she flashes golden sticks at them. That is lightning, and it is very dangerous."

Molly was trying to hide her fear by showing off her knowledge. Babou did not seem the least bit impressed. So, she began to explain what was really bothering her.

"My sisters and I are petrified of thunder and lightning. At the first rumble from the sky, we crowd behind the couch or squeeze in behind the toilet, hoping our mama or dada will come and comfort us. I must return home immediately. I can't leave them alone in a thunderstorm," she said.

"Hold on, then, Molly!" Babou said. "Hold on! I am going to take you back home!"

Moments later, a strong breeze arose and coursed through the forest. The branches of the trees began to whip and sway crazily, and the rain spat heavy drops. The rising wind seemed to make Babou go all the faster, as if he were part of it. Molly was too scared to enjoy the ride. At one point, Babou stumbled and almost fell over the broken root of a tree that was sticking up from the ground. Molly dug her dewclaws deeper into each side of Babou's neck, desperately trying to stop herself from tumbling to the ground.

As they traveled along the edge of the pond, the beating of Babou's fierce gallop startled the Canada geese. They flew up in a big hubbub of honking and yakking.

Babou stopped some distance short of the little bridge. Bending low on all fours, he let Molly climb down onto the ground.

"Thank you so much, Babou," Molly said with relief.

By the time Molly reached the stairs leading up to the veranda, the storm had died out just as quickly as it had begun. Mama slid the door open and waited for Molly on the deck.

"Where have you been?" she scolded her, as she stepped through the sliding glass door. "With all the thunder and lightning, we were worried about you."

Rags and Pups rushed toward Molly, their tails wagging happily. Suddenly, an expression of fear came into Pupsie's eyes. The hackles stood up on her back. She had picked up the scent of Babou on Molly's coat. Molly knew this was bound to happen sooner or later. "Don't say anything," she said, as she growled ferociously at Pupsie.

"Oh, Molly! That's not nice to growl at Pupsie like that," Mama said.

Molly was deeply offended. She depended so much on mama's love and understanding since she was a tiny puppy. After her adopted sisters had arrived in the house, she wanted more than ever to keep that special place she had in her heart. Being told off by mama in front of Rags and Pupsie was more than she could take. She turned on her heels and went to lie down behind her palm tree in the sunroom. No one would disturb her there, not even mama or dada.

Mama was right, of course. She should never have been nasty to Pups. Yet how was she going to explain to her and Rags why she had the scent of a bear on her? *I will not try*, she decided. *It will remain my secret. Thank goodness, mama and dada are not able to pick up dog language or smell Babou's scent.*

Chapter Eight

A King in Hiding

A full cycle of the moon had passed since Molly had first encountered Babou. Each day, they had roamed the forest together. They had seen the mallards come and go on the pond, having used it as a temporary rest on their long migratory journey south. The miniscule hummingbirds had long ceased visiting mama's hibiscus flowers and had returned to Mexico to spend the winter. All the trees of the forest were naked except for the evergreens and the pepper-toned red oaks. The fallen leaves had dressed the earth in a luxuriant red and gold carpet.

"Ready for the ride?" Molly called out cheerfully as she saw Babou standing by their usual rendezvous.

Babou looked at her without answering. After a long while, she finally broke the silence.

"What is the matter, Babou? you seem so sad."

"The time has come for me to go, Molly," he mumbled softly.

Nothing had prepared her to hear him say anything like this. Somehow, she pulled herself together and asked, "Go where?"

"To the mountains up north," he said simply.

The thought of his leaving was slow to penetrate Molly's mind. "Why, Babou? Why?"

"It is the law of bears, Molly. I must find a den, and I must find it soon, before winter sets in."

"What's a den?"

"It is a secret place where I can hide, like a cave in a mountainside, or in the hollow trunk of a large, dead tree."

Molly felt a glimmer of hope. "I could help you find one around here. Friends help friends!" she said excitedly. "That would be fun, and I could come and visit you."

"No, Molly, no! It would have to be far, far away, away from houses and hunters, somewhere deep in the forest. It has to be a safe place where I can sleep undisturbed for a few months until spring returns."

Overcome by a sense of frustration, Molly snapped, "Don't you get enough sleep every night? Why on earth would you want to sleep for a few months?"

Babou looked up at the gently nodding leaves that remained on the old oak tree. "Like many wild animals, I have to hibernate during the winter months, Molly, because there is no food left in the forest for me to eat."

Visions of Babou happily stuffing himself with berries came to Molly's mind. At the same time, she recalled how hard and long he had to search the forest to find food, not like her and her sisters. Mama always made sure there was food enough for them all.

Molly could not resist making one more desperate attempt.

"Babou, please don't go!"

"But I have to, Molly."

"You could get lost."

"No, Molly, never. This is my forest. I have to cope with the perils of life alone. Nobody can protect me or defend me, not even you, my dear friend."

She was speechless. Perhaps, at last, she was beginning to understand what a king really was! On the surface, Babou had often struck her as slow in thought, yet she now knew that he was a master in handling his own problems.

Babou had obviously made up his mind. Although Molly was distraught, she would never want to see him placed in an unsafe situation. Yet, she could not bear the thought of his leaving. She stepped toward him. He bent down, as if he were going to take her for a ride. Molly rubbed his muzzle gently with her paw. There was a little twinkle in his eyes.

"Molly, don't be sad!"

She wanted to ask him whether he would come back to see her. She didn't, because she knew that right now, nothing could soften the deep sorrow she was feeling.

Babou slowly stretched his legs, turned, and then gave one of his funny little bouncing flips in the air. As he set off, the carpet of autumn leaves swirled once more into the deep-blue sky. Molly stood motionless and watched him lope away through the woods until he vanished out of sight.

Chapter Nine

Pupsie's Howling

Along, wavy ribbon of Canada geese honked loudly like an out-of-tune band of trumpet players. Molly, Rags, and Pupsie looked up sharply into the sky. Spring was on its way.

It had been a harsh, snowy winter, but for the dogs, snow-time was playtime. They liked to chase one another in ever-widening circles with the speed of antelopes in flight, sailing over any obstacle in their path or diving headlong into the deep, white powder. Best of all, they liked to bury their muzzles in the snow and savor its hidden smells beneath. Mmm! Nothing could quite match a real ice topping.

Pupsie wandered off onto the neighbor's land and suddenly started to howl desolately. Molly knew—only the smell of a bear could set Pupsie off like this! It was a doleful sound that brought back a primitive genetic reminder from one hundred thousand years ago, when the dog and the gray wolf shared the same ancestor.

Could it be Babou? Molly wondered. *Had he come back during the night and crossed the bridge, something he had faithfully promised me he would never do?* She had thought of him often during the long winter months and had missed him so much. *Had he found himself a den? Had he been able to find enough food to get him through the winter's hibernation? What if it wasn't Babou? What if it was another bear that had trespassed onto our land? This could turn out to be dangerous.*

With terror in their eyes, Rags and Pupsie dashed back home. Molly stayed behind to check out the bear's scent. She swept the ground with her nose, and in no time, she determined that it was definitely Babou who had come visiting. His lingering scent on the grass was unmistakable. Her heart raced with anticipation. Babou, her friend, had returned.

She rushed across the humpback bridge. As she approached Babou's old oak tree, she caught sight of his gigantic silhouette high up in the branches. She watched him as he slithered down the trunk of the tree with his black paws and forelegs tightly wrapped around the lower branches like tread-worn truck tires.

"Molly!" Babou's familiar voice called out. "It is so nice to see you again. How are you?"

Molly was so upset that she did not answer his question.

"Why did you cross the bridge and come on our land? You had promised me you would never do that."

"I know, Molly. I know I broke my promise. I'm sorry, but it was urgent that I see you, and I couldn't think of any other way of letting you know that I had come back from up north."

"What could be so urgent, Babou?"

"Let me show you," he answered, as a troubled expression loomed across his face.

Molly strained her eye to see more clearly. She could make out a small, fluffy ball of fur. "What is that?"

"She's a bear cub—"

"*A bear cub*?" Molly interrupted sharply. "Where did you get it?"

"I found her up north, in the mountains," he replied simply.

Molly remembered that Babou was often short in his use of words. Trying not to show her impatience, she continued. "What I *really* meant, Babou, was, *how* did you find this creature—this cub—and why do you have it with you now?"

"When I first woke up from my long winter sleep," Babou began, "I was so, so hungry. I wandered through the forest day after day, trying to find food. Then one day, I heard a mournful whimper coming from deep inside the hollow trunk of a huge tree that had fallen to the ground. I bent down and looked inside."

"And what did you find?" Molly asked with impatience.

"A mama bear with two tiny cubs on her tummy. One was a male, and the other was this little one, his twin sister, who was fussing and crying non-stop." He gently gripped the cub in his teeth by the scruff of her neck, and placed her down on the ground close to Molly.

"But the mama bear and the other cub were silent and motionless. When I reached in and touched them, I realized they were as hard and cold as ice."

"You mean … they were dead?" Molly hesitated in horror.

"Yes!"

"That is terrible, Babou. Why do you think they died?"

"I do not know, Molly. Perhaps the mama became ill and she and the other little one starved to death."

"Starved to death!" Molly said distressed.

"So I took this little one with me. She screamed her head off when I first picked her up, but gradually, she calmed down and got used to me."

Babou had such a big heart, Molly remembered.

"I soon realized that I was faced with a really big problem," Babou continued. "The cub would not eat the same things as I did," he added sadly. "She didn't want any of the leaf buds I picked for her from the tree branches, and it was too early in the spring to find berries or nuts in the forest. She even turned her nose up at the big, juicy bugs and beetles I dug out for her from under the rocks."

Molly refrained from saying that she was not surprised. She certainly would not want to eat those sorts of things, either.

"She hardly eats anything at all, and I am scared she is going to die like her twin brother and her mother," Babou said, his voice deep with concern.

Molly could think of nothing to say.

"I know I should not have broken my promise and crossed the bridge, but I was desperate. You are my only friend. Can you help me, Molly?"

It immediately crossed her mind that Babou had not come back to see her, but only to get her help. Her feelings were hurt. Yet, looking down at the helpless little creature curled up next to her, she wondered why she was so selfish. Molly could only reply, "I must go, Babou. Mama will be wondering where I am."

"The cub doesn't have a name yet, Molly," Babou called after her. "Can you give her one?"

This was the least of Molly's concerns. Before crossing the bridge, she looked back. Babou had picked up the cub by the scruff of her neck, ready to climb back to the top of the tree. Molly felt a twinge of jealousy. This was not the reunion she had been waiting for all winter long.

Chapter Ten

In Search of Coconuts

Molly rushed up the stairs of the balcony and barked impatiently for mama to come and let her in.

"You have been out for such a long time," mama complained.

If you only knew, Molly thought as she pushed her way past mama's legs.

She went to stretch out on the floor under the kitchen table to rest and ponder Babou's problem.

Dada was talking to someone on the phone. He often got calls from chimpanzee and monkey sanctuaries, asking for his advice on all sorts of health problems. Like so many dogs, Molly seemed to instinctively understand the principle of how telephones worked.

All of a sudden, she perked up her ears. An odd word here and there, like *baby* and *milk*, caught her attention. Judging from the tone of dada's voice, this call was a very serious one. She listened extra carefully.

In a very concerned voice, dada said, "But if you think the mother has no milk, you will have to feed the baby yourself. Yes, of course! You bet!" Then dada added, "Yep, I assure you, without milk, the baby will die."

Molly sprang to her paws. The message was clear: Babou's orphaned cub would die without milk. She rushed to the sliding glass door and grumbled and groaned for someone to let her out.

Mama wiped her wet hands on a dishtowel, left the potatoes she was peeling at the kitchen sink, and came to let Molly out. "What is wrong with you today, Molly?" she said in exasperation. "You keep coming and going! You are like a yo-yo!"

Molly paid no heed to what mama was saying as she scampered down the stairs of the balcony and made her way to the woods as fast as she could go. Babou must have heard her coming and was already clambering down the trunk of the old tree, obviously surprised to see her return so soon.

He had left the little one asleep on one of the broad branches, high up in the tree.

"Babou, I've found the answer," Molly barked with excitement. "You have to give the cub milk. She must have m-i-l-k to drink!" she said, stretching the word out.

"Milk?" Babou called out in bewilderment. "But only mama bears have milk, Molly."

"Yes! How silly of me," she said. Babou was right; Molly had not stopped to consider the practical details.

At that moment, the cub uttered a most pitiful cry. Babou rushed back up the tree to fetch her. She was so weak. He snatched her up by the scruff of her neck in his massive jaws to bring her down.

When he reached the ground, Molly noticed how forlorn the cub looked. Her eyes were closed, her coat was all matted and dirty, and her skinny little body seemed totally defenseless. For the first time, Molly's heart went out to her. "Milk, milk, where can we find milk?" she kept saying to herself. "She is certainly going to die very soon if we can't find milk."

A thought crossed Molly's mind.

"Babou, I seem to remember my mama once telling a friend about coconut trees in Jamaica. She was complaining about how cold the winter was here and how she wished she could be back in Jamaica right then, drinking coconut milk."

"Molly, how can we get the milk from the trees?"

Climbing for coconuts

"My mama explained how the young boys in Jamaica shimmy up the tall trees with their bare hands and feet to get to the coconuts that grow in clusters at the very top. Then, they split them open with big knives to get the milk out. Mama said it tasted so good."

Babou scratched his forehead, obviously trying to rake his brain. "I've seen hickory nuts and chestnuts," he said. "And I know what oak trees and maple trees look like, but I don't think I've seen a coconut tree that makes milk. Where would we find one, Molly?"

"I'm not sure; I think my mama said they grew along the edge of the beaches in Jamaica."

"Well, maybe they grow along the banks of the lakes here in the forest, and I just never noticed them," Babou said enthusiastically. "I know all the lakes around here. Jump on my back with the cub, Molly, and let's go and take a look."

"Why not?" Molly said cheerily.

Gently, Babou pulled the cub's paws on his nape and Molly climbed onto his back as she pushed the cub from behind with her nose to keep her from falling off.

"Your bark is my command!" Babou called out.

Molly was happy that he had not forgotten.

"Ready, steady, go for the coconut trees!" she barked, holding on tightly to the cub.

Turning his head toward her, Babou said, "You know, Molly, the little cub still does not have a name. I was hoping you would give her one."

"Coco," she said, as the name just popped into her head. "Let's call her Coco."

"Coco," Babou repeated in his hoarse, deep voice. "That is such a beautiful name." With that, he stamped his feet, sprang into the air, and gave one of his funny little turns, and off they set for the lakes.

Chapter Eleven

The Shrinking Forest

Molly was thrilled to explore the forest again with Babou. Despite her attempts to forget him, she had longed for their wild rides together in the woods and the wonderful feeling of the wind streaming through her hair. This time, they had an important mission to accomplish: saving Coco's life. Molly held the little cub beneath her body to keep her warm. She could feel her heart beat, but for how long? It brought back memories when she would look after orphaned baby chimps that her dada would bring home when they were sick.

They passed a group of deer that was reaching up to devour the delicate, pink flower buds from the lower branches of the maple trees. They looked so terribly skinny. The winter had been hard on them.

Eventually, they reached a beautiful, long, narrow lake. A pair of graceful wood ducks glided silently on the water, while a gaggle of Canada geese dipped their long necks deep beneath the surface in search of weeds to eat. The delicate songs of countless warblers, who were busy building their nests, filled the air with magic.

Babou circled the shore, slowing down every now and again to get a better chance of spotting a coconut palm amongst all the other trees. None of the trees looked anything like the ones that Molly had described.

A little further on, a rather hairless, scraggy-looking creature, with a string of tiny babies hanging from her back, was lying on the ground.

Mrs. O'Possum

"What is that?" Molly asked Babou as softly as she could.

"That's an opossum," he whispered.

"Hello, Mrs. O'Possum," Babou called out. "How is your family?"

"It has been a terrible winter, Mr. Bear. Food is scarce and my babies are starving. It wasn't so bad when they were tiny and lived in my pouch. They had plenty of milk to drink then. Now they have grown, so I walk endlessly in search of grubs and worms for them to eat."

"How many babies do you have to feed?" Babou asked.

"I don't exactly know. More than a dozen, I'd say."

Molly looked at Babou in amazement. *That's an awful lot of babies for a mama to look after,* she thought.

"Hold on just a little longer, Mrs. O'Possum, spring is just around the corner, and soon everything will be fine."

"Who is with you today?" the opossum inquired.

"Oh, this is my friend, Molly. She is helping me with this orphaned little bear cub I am looking after. Let me ask you a question, Mrs. O'Possum. You know the forest very well. Where could we find a coconut tree?"

"A coconut tree?" she thought for a while and then said, "I've never seen such a tree. Good day, Mr. Bear." She turned on her heels and ambled off.

Molly asked Babou, "What did Mrs. O'Possum mean when she mentioned her babies being in her pouch?"

"When baby opossums are first born, they are hardly bigger than a purple blueberry," Babou replied.

"That seems impossible. How do they survive?"

"They crawl into their mother's pouch, which is like a soft, warm pocket on the wall of her tummy. They attach their little mouths to their mother's nipples that line the inside of her pouch."

Remembering how difficult it was for her to get to her own mother's nipples, Molly asked, "can they all get milk?"

"Yes, they remain safe and warm and well fed until they grow large enough to be able to ride around on their mother's back like the ones we just saw. Life then begins to get hard for them. Many of them die, as Mrs. O'Possum told us, because they cannot find solid food to eat."

There are so many strange animals living in the forest, Molly thought, *but Babou seems to know about them all*.

Coyote on the hunt

At the edge of the lake, Molly spied what looked to her like a dog lapping the water. He had pointed ears and a tufted tail.

"What's that up ahead?" Molly said as quietly as she could.

"That's a coyote," Babou muttered. "He's a sort of wild dog."

The coyote lifted his head, water dripping from his chin, and called out to Babou, "Where are you off to, Mr. Bear?"

"We are trying to find a coconut tree," Babou replied.

"A *what*?" exclaimed the coyote.

"A coconut tree," repeated Babou. "and you?"

"I am hunting for rabbits," he answered, as he eyed Coco on Babou's back with obvious relish.

Molly became scared. "Let's go, Babou," she whispered. "I don't like the look in his eyes." Without any farewell, they left the coyote.

"Let me show you one more lake, Molly. Maybe we will be lucky and find some coconut trees there."

At that very moment, a deep, vibrant rumble shook the earth. Babou came to an instant halt.

"Do you know what that is, Babou?" Molly asked in shock.

"It sounds like thunder," he replied.

"No, it is dynamite."

"Dynamite? What is dynamite, Molly?"

"It is a powder that builders use to break up the big rock formations in the ground to clear the forest so they can lay the floors for their new houses. They drill holes in the rock, fill them with the dynamite powder, and then blow them up."

"How do you know so much about dynamite, Molly?" Babou asked in amazement.

"I heard my dada talk about it to mama the other night. Let's not go any further. It is dangerous."

As they rounded the corner of a huge face of rock protruding from the steep mountainside, Molly and Babou let out a gasp of horror. There was hardly a tree that had not been cut down and strewn in endless piles of destruction.

No delicate twitters of bird songs were to be heard in this little valley. Again, a booming rumble suddenly rocked the ground beneath their feet.

"Let's go right now, or we could get killed," Molly said.

Babou turned and rushed back to his oak tree with Molly and the little Coco. The sun was now low in the sky, the shadows of the trees long on the ground.

"What are we going to do?" Babou lamented.

"I really do not know. I don't have an answer," Molly replied.

With a heavy heart, she headed home for the night.

Chapter Twelve

A Long, Sleepless Night

Molly tossed and turned all night long, which woke mama up repeatedly. Mama whispered softly into her ear each time. "Everything is okay, my little one. You have to sleep."

How could she sleep? She could not stop thinking of Coco, who might not survive the night. She was faced with a problem she never had before—having to help a friend in need. How could a little dog like her do that? She realized that her mama and dada had cared for her all her life, and she had never had to struggle for anything. Dada had given her the blood transfusion that had saved her life when she was a tiny puppy. Mama had looked after her through the nights when she was weak and frail and needed special care. They both had given her not just shelter and food, but even more important, endless love.

Babou had received none of these things. He was Molly's friend and now his problems had become hers. Somehow, she would have to find a way of helping him. *But how?* she kept asking herself. *How?*

When the pale light of dawn eventually came, Molly had barely slept. Tired, she stumbled her way down the stairs to the kitchen, along with mama and dada and her two sisters.

Molly's mind was fixed on Coco. Without waiting for breakfast, she whined and fussed at the balcony door to be let out. Mama stood up from the kitchen table and sleepily made her way to open the door.

"You know," she said to dada, "Molly has been acting very strangely lately. Have you noticed? I can't understand what's got into her."

"Cabin fever after the long, cold winter," dada suggested between yawns.

"No, I think it is more serious than that," mama replied.

In no time, Molly reached Babou. He was standing at the foot of the oak tree, a troubled expression on his face, a lifeless-looking Coco at his feet.

"How is Coco?" Molly called out.

"She's in a bad state, Molly. During the night, she became so cold that she fell into a deep sleep, and now I don't seem to be able to wake her up."

"She's in a coma," Molly said, not quite sure that she fully understood the meaning of the word. She had heard her dada telling people how she used to go into a coma when she was a puppy, and that he thought she was going to die. "I remember once waking up in the middle of the night," Molly recalled, "finding dada injecting something clear, like water, into the blood in my foreleg through a long, plastic tube. As the liquid dripped in, I became more awake and started to feel better, and I was able to stand up."

"Maybe that is what Coco needs," said Babou.

Before she could answer, Molly heard Rags and Pupsie barking from somewhere way off in the distance. "My sisters must have followed me, wondering what I was up to," Molly said, staring at Babou in panic.

"Molly!" Pupsie yapped, as she and Rags burst into the clearing in the woods just moments later. "Why didn't you wait for breakfast? Why did—"

At that instant, Pupsie and Rags both came to a dead standstill. They had seen Babou. Overcome with instant terror, Pupsie stood with one front paw raised in the air, the hackles down the length of her neck and back standing menacingly erect. She looked like a ferocious hyena about to attack a lion. Rags, frozen in sudden fear, began a long, low, rumbling growl. *Trouble is imminent*, Molly thought, *if I do not act quickly*. "It's all right, Rags and Pupsie. Everything is okay," she shouted.

Rags' long, rolling growl intensified, and Pupsie began a high-pitched whine. *Would they dare to attack Babou?* Molly wondered. *If so, it will turn into a terrible fight.*

Babou started to groan in a most threatening pitch, sensing he was cornered. "I think I should leave, Molly," he said.

"No, don't go," Molly pleaded. "Rags and Pups, this is Babou. He's my friend and he needs our help. He won't hurt you, I promise. He has just returned from the mountains up north with this tiny, orphaned bear cub named Coco. She is weak and is not eating anything. She is going to starve to death if we cannot quickly find milk to give her."

Slowly, Pupsie's hackles began to go down, and Rags stopped growling. Babou stood still. The crisis had passed.

Chapter Thirteen

Sharing Memories and Ideas

Rags stepped forward a little hesitantly and approached Coco. She sniffed her all over and then began to gently lick the lifeless little cub from head to toe.

Rags had always been good with baby animals. It must have been the sheepdog genes in her. When dada brought home baby rabbits he found abandoned in the woods, or robin chicks that had fallen out of their nests, or a family of deer mice who took up residence in the house in winter, Rags stayed with them all the time. She had so much patience. She liked to gently nuzzle them with her nose, as if she were herding a flock of sheep.

Molly with Mystery

Before her sisters had been adopted, Molly helped dada rear Mystery, a baby chimp who had been abandoned by his mother. He liked to rough-and-tumble with Molly, pulling her by her ears and tail. Back and forth in endless play, Molly would retaliate by grabbing Mystery's T-shirt in her teeth and dragging him the length of the kitchen floor, until mama would tell them to behave themselves and stop. After a while, Mystery would become so exhausted that he would fall asleep, and Molly would proudly watch over him.

Molly explained to Rags and Pupsie about Babou's and her own failure to find a coconut tree to get the milk from inside the nuts.

Rags on her mountaintop

"Have you tried to feed her hermit crabs?" Rags asked with a wag of her tail. "I lived on a mountaintop on a sunny island in the Caribbean for three months when I was young, until mama and dada found me and brought me home with them. My owner had abandoned me because I had been a 'bad dog.' All I had to eat were hermit crabs. They would get squashed on the road by passing cars, and I'd climb down the mountain each morning from the nest I had made in the jungle bush and scrape them off the road with my teeth."

"I don't think we would find hermit crabs around here," Molly said.

Pupsie on her garbage dump

"What about taking Coco to a garbage dump?" Pupsie suggested. "I was also abandoned by my owners, on a garbage dump on a Caribbean island along with four big, nasty dogs when I was a puppy," she explained, all full of herself, "before mama and dada came and rescued me. Each day, I would wait for the big truck to come and dump all its new garbage on top of what was already there. Then I would crawl frantically over the pile in search of scraps to eat. Immediately, the grown-up dogs would attack me and bite me all over. Even the seagulls—hundreds of them, screaming and squabbling amongst themselves all the time—would swoop down and peck me in the hope of stealing whatever food I had found."

"I like garbage dumps," Babou interrupted, very proud of himself. "I get some of my best food there, but I couldn't get Coco to eat any of it. It's not that I *didn't* try, believe me."

"It is not garbage that she needs, it is milk," Molly said firmly.

"I've got an idea," Pupsie barked, wagging her tail furiously, obviously quite pleased with herself for making what she thought was going to be a major contribution to the discussion. "Molly, why don't you tell dada about the problem? Maybe he can come up with a solution."

"How am I going to tell dada?" Molly replied, a little annoyed that Pupsie could be so silly. "How would I make him understand what I was saying? To most human beings, one dog's bark is the same as another's."

"You're right," Pupsie agreed, her tail drawn in between her legs.

"I know a way," Rags chimed in. "Let's go back home together and try to make dada follow us back into the woods. We can show him Coco, and he'll understand the problem for himself straight away."

"Yes, yes!" Pupsie said in quick little yaps. "That's a great idea."

"Okay," Molly agreed, surprised that Rags would come up with such a good solution and a little shamefaced that she hadn't thought of it herself.

"Babou, you stay here with Coco at the foot of the tree. Don't wander off. We'll try to be back as fast as we can with our dada. Let's keep our claws crossed!"

Chapter Fourteen

Making Dada Understand

The three dogs returned home in great haste, desperate to find dada. Molly led the search.

"Rags, go and check the garage and the basement. Pups, check to see if he is working on the computer."

In no time, they were back.

"Yap, yap, he is not there."

"Let's all go to the bathroom upstairs," Molly suggested.

The bathroom door was closed. Molly scratched the bottom of it with her front claws to let dada know that she was outside and wanted to come in.

"Who's there?" dada called out as he opened the door. "Well, well!" he said with a laugh. "It's little Miss Molly!"

Dada was still in his pajamas and had a towel wrapped around his neck. His face was covered in a frothy, white lather of shaving cream.

Molly forced her way into the bathroom. She sat to one side of his legs, looking up at him, drumming her tail on the floor in rhythmic fashion to catch his attention.

"What's up, Molly?" he said, looking down at her. "I didn't think you liked anything to do with bathrooms. What do you want, my little dog? certainly not a bath, I'm sure of that."

The sound of the word *bath* made Molly tremble all over. She regained control of herself and gave a couple of quick snorts, flicking her muzzle from side to side, as if she was about to sneeze. That was her way of making dada realize that she had something very important to tell him and that he should pay attention to her.

"What is Molly trying to tell me?" he said. "I don't understand."

It was always so frustrating for Molly when she had to explain things to dada, knowing he would not understand.

Dada picked up the razor and began to shave the whiskers on his chin. His mouth twisted from one side of his face to the other, and his nose twitched as if he had a fly tickling it.

Suddenly, Rags and Pupsie pushed their way into the bathroom and sat on the other side of his legs, staring up at him. "What is this?" he said in amazement. "The *three* little dogs! What on earth do they want? Surely, they're not interested in watching dada shave?"

The Caribbean trio in discussion

Molly snorted and snuffled again, flicking her head from side to side with even more exaggerated motion. Rags began to stamp her paws up and down on the tiled floor, as she always does when she is frustrated. Pupsie, obviously not quite sure what the other two expected her to do, bounced up and down like a jack-in-the-box.

"What is this?" dada repeated, even more mystified. "Do you want to go for a *walk* in the car?" he asked, the expression that the three dogs had coined for "a *ride* in the car."

Instantly, Rags, Pupsie, and Molly began to jump up and down with excitement. At last, they had got dada's attention.

"But I haven't had my shower yet," dada lamented. "Okay, okay," he said in resignation as he began to wipe the shaving cream off his face.

He quickly pulled on a sweater and a pair of jogging pants over his pajamas and made his way down the stairs. All three dogs were crowding around his ankles in excitement, wagging their tails furiously and pressing against his legs as they tried to beat him down the stairs.

They ran out the sliding door and tumbled down the balcony stairs, almost tripping dada over. He turned left toward the garage and the three dogs rushed in the opposite direction, toward the bridge and the woods.

"What's wrong with those little dogs?" dada shouted after them in surprise. "I thought they wanted to go for a *walk* in the car!"

The three dogs crossed the bridge, totally ignoring dada's remark.

"They want to go to the woods? Wait for me, then, those little dogs!" dada called out. "Wait for me!"

Chapter Fifteen

Running Out of Time

They all became excited when dada crossed the bridge. They had finally got him to do exactly what they wanted. Rags continued to jump up and down, her tongue hanging out and her eyes all a sparkle, obviously proud of herself. Her plan had worked.

Rushing to meet Babou

"What's special about going for a walk in the woods so early this morning?" dada asked as he followed them along the trail.

Yapping like a young puppy, Molly stumbled backward and looked constantly up into dada's eyes, trying to keep his attention focused on her and her sisters. She was afraid that he might turn around and go back home at any moment.

"Oh, my goodness," dada gasped, all of a sudden stopping dead in his tracks. "There's a bear! A huge bear!" he shouted. "Molly, Rags, Pupsie, come back! Now! Quickly! *Immediately!"* he continued to stammer, without taking his eyes off the bear.

Molly jumped up and down, barking and looking up into dada's face, to make him realize that everything was all right. Rags and Pupsie ran forward and sat right next to Babou to show they were not scared of him. With beaming grins on their faces, their tongues hanging out the sides of their mouths in happiness, they turned to look at dada. "Woof!" and "Ruff!" they barked and yapped in unison.

Dada stood frozen, obviously not understanding how the three dogs could be so close to this huge bear, yet seeming not to be the least bit afraid of him. Then, he noticed the little, black furry mass among the tangle of ground cover next to the adult bear's huge feet. "I can't believe my eyes! It's a bear cub."

Dada was terrified. One wrong move on his part and the adult bear might attack him. Rags started to lick Coco all over, from head to claw. With the greatest difficulty, she picked Coco up in her mouth and half carried, half dragged her motionless body to dada's feet.

Not sure of how the big bear would react to this, dada stiffened with fear.

"I think your dada is afraid of me, Molly," Babou said softly, so that only she could hear. "I should go back up the tree and hide myself." And, he began to slowly climb the tree, from branch to branch, obviously trying not to make any noise.

Dada looked down at the lifeless, furry ball that Rags had laid at his feet. He bent down slowly, glancing up frequently at the big bear.

The three dogs crowded around him, eager to see what he was going to do with Coco. Babou did not take his eyes off Coco.

Dada began to gently run his hands over the cub's body. "She's very thin and weak, this little thing," he said out loud. "Her ribs are sticking out. She is like a skeleton. Her eyes are open, so she must be at least one month old."

Listening as intently as he could without a stethoscope, he picked the cub up in his hands and held her chest close to his ear. "She reminds me of you, Molly, when you were a tiny little puppy, when mama and I first found you. This little cub's lungs are gurgling, just like yours were."

"Come over and listen!" dada said. Molly proudly came right next to Coco's chest. Her face cringed when she heard the gurgles. "She has severe pneumonia, Molly, just as you had back then."

Dada felt her sunken tummy and noticed that her gums and tongue were a dirty gray rather than a healthy, bright pink. He concluded that she was also severely anemic.

"She's going to die if we can't find a way to feed her and treat her pneumonia and anemia," dada said as he looked sadly at the dogs.

"Rags and Pupsie, you stay here with the cub to guard her and make sure she does not get cold," Dada said.

"What's he saying? What's he saying?" Pupsie asked as she stared into Rags' eyes.

"Snuffle, snort," Rags calmly responded. She had understood dada.

"Molly, you come home with me and we'll put together all the things we will need to treat the cub. Won't be long," dada said to Rags and Pups like he does when he has to leave the dogs at home to do some errands. "I promise, won't be long!"

He looked at his wristwatch. It was already past ten o'clock. Time was running out for Coco.

Chapter Sixteen

Emergency Treatment in the Forest

"You'll never believe it," dada said excitedly as he and Molly got back to the house.

"Believe what?" mama said.

"There's a huge black bear with a tiny cub in the woods."

"Oh, my goodness! Where are Rags and Pupsie?" she replied in panic. She grabbed her cheeks with both hands as she realized that only Molly had come back with him.

"Don't get upset; they are fine," dada said.

Molly wagged her tail as she reached up to mama with her outstretched paw and looked deeply into her eyes. *If only I could explain to mama that dada hadn't just left Rags and Pupsie in danger*, she thought.

"I don't have time to tell you the whole story, but the cub is very weak, almost unconscious. She's probably going to die within the next few hours if I am not able to make her turn around."

Molly wagged her tail in agreement and gave a little bark.

"Rags and Pupsie have stayed behind with the big bear to keep the cub warm until we return with food and some medicines to treat her."

A mother rhesus monkey with her baby

"I can't believe what you are telling me," mama said in a horrified tone. "You know that wild animals are very protective of their babies. Bears can be dangerous, especially if they have a cub. How could you have left Rags and Pupsie in the woods with a bear?"

"It sounds unbelievable, but the three dogs seem to have made friends with the bear. I haven't the faintest idea how they succeeded, but they *have*," dada insisted. "That's why they wanted me to follow them into the forest earlier this morning, to see with my own eyes what the situation was with the little cub. They are very clever dogs, when you think about it." Molly yapped with pride, but mama was still not convinced.

"Something else I don't understand," she said. "How would the mother let you get close enough to be able to do anything to the cub?"

"Believe it or not, the mother climbed up the tree and left the baby behind on the ground. Perhaps the dogs told the bear to do that. I really don't know."

"Oh, come on! I can't imagine a mother bear leaving her baby down like that," mama said, shaking her head in disbelief. "And are you trying to tell me that dogs and bears can communicate with each other?"

"I know, I know," dada said. "I don't understand it, either, but they can certainly do better than me," he responded in frustration.

"I think you could get badly injured," mama said.

"But Molly and Rags and the Pupsie will make sure I don't get hurt. I know they will. They somehow seem to trust the bear, and the bear trusts them. Any rate, I must try to save the cub. Let's gather what I need," dada concluded with an air of finality.

Mama sighed. After a while, she added, "Okay! Let's see. We still have milk bottles and nipples from the time when we reared Mystery," she said as she searched through one of the kitchen cabinets. "I could warm up some soy milk and add a small amount of oatmeal to give it a bit of body."

"That's a good idea," dada said. "While you do that, I'll check my emergency box. I'm sure the cub's blood-sugar level is dangerously low, so I will have to give some sugar solution under the skin. I should also be prepared to give her an injection of antibiotic."

In no time, mama had a warm bottle of milk with oatmeal prepared.

"Good luck!" she said with fear in her voice, as they were about to leave.

She turned to Molly and stared deeply into her eyes. "Make sure dada doesn't do anything dangerous, my little one."

If I could only make mama and dada understand, Molly thought.

She wagged her tail gently, and she and dada rushed back to the woods.

Chapter Seventeen

Not Out of the Woods Yet

Babou kept Coco as warm as possible, tucked up under his tummy. Rags and Pups were lying next to the cub, trying to plug any gaps between Babou's tummy and the ground. Babou saw dada and Molly coming, and he started to climb back up the tree.

Dada approached very cautiously, still keeping one eye on the adult bear up in the tree, the other on the motionless cub lying on the ground. He gently picked Coco up in his hands and examined her with his stethoscope. Her body was limp, and her lungs sounded even worse than he had at first thought.

Dada began to have second thoughts about trying to give the cub the bottle of milk by mouth. "She is too weak; I dare not risk it," he said out loud. "If she coughs or gags as she swallows, some of the milk might go down into her lungs and there would be nothing I could do to save her. She would die. I would sooner give her the sugar solution under her skin. It would at least provide her with some immediate energy. And let's not forget the injection of antibiotic to fight off her pneumonia," he said as a reminder to himself.

"All done, all over!" he finally announced when he had finished the long, slow process. "Not good!" he sighed. "Not good at all! the cub's condition is 'touch and go.'"

Dada looked at his wristwatch. "We have been away so long! mama is going to think that something terrible has happened. Would Rags and Pupsie stay with the cub again," dada asked, "while Molly and I go home for a short time? Don't forget to keep the little cub warm, my little ones, and give her lots of kisses."

Later, when dada came back with Molly, Babou was already up in his tree. Pupsie and Rags had Coco snuggled in between them. Dada picked her up, and the three dogs looked into his eyes to see if he had noticed any sign of improvement. There was none, but at least she was still alive.

"We cannot give up hope," he said, looking back at the three dogs.

"Let's get her more sugar solution under her skin. She is still far too weak for me to risk giving her milk."

From his tree, Babou could sense that Coco's situation was very bad, and he started to moan softly.

"What is going to happen to Coco?" he asked Molly.

"I am sure my dada will not give up and that he will come back to treat her."

After a while she added with pride, "he has treated many different animals all over the world."

Dada (3rd left) treats an injured elephant in India

Dada gathered his medical supplies, and the three dogs followed him back home, their tails drooping. Before they reached the bridge, they heard Babou coming down his tree to take care of Coco.

A few hours later, they returned. They dreaded to find Coco dead. To dada's surprise, the cub was livelier than he would ever have expected. She responded to touch and sounds, and you could tell that she really enjoyed when Rags and Pupsie licked her all over.

"Would this little cub like some milk to drink?" dada said. He held her upright in his lap as he crouched on his haunches.

He gently pushed the soft rubber nipple of the milk bottle into her mouth. At first, the cub spat the nipple from her lips, but after a while, dada managed to calm her down and she began to rhythmically suck the warm milk. The more she sucked, the stronger she became. "That is very good, my little one," dada repeated over and over in a soothing voice. The dogs watched very closely, and Babou looked down from his tree and made happy little grunting sounds every time Coco swallowed some milk.

"We'll come back again to give her more milk and another dose of antibiotics," dada said, hoping that the big bear would somehow understand. "Come on, Molly, Rags, and Pupsie. Let's go home!"

On entering the house, dada shouted out to mama, "she drank all her milk."

"That's wonderful!" she replied.

Dada and the three dogs returned before it was dark to feed the cub and give her the last injection of antibiotic for the night. She was making encouraging progress, but she was still not "out of the woods."

Chapter Eighteen

Listening under the Table

That evening, Molly was lying under the kitchen table, as she often does, listening intently to mama and dada talking and trying her best to understand what they were saying. Rags and Pups were so exhausted from the events of the day that they had already gone upstairs to bed.

"How old do you think the cub is?" mama asked.

"Hard to say," dada replied. "If I'm not mistaken, bear cubs are born around the end of January, beginning of February. So, it's mid-April now—she must be at least two months old."

"How big is she?"

"Probably less than two pounds. Again, if I remember correctly, cubs weigh one pound or less at birth."

"That's incredibly small," mama said in surprise.

"You will not believe this, but the mothers often give birth while they are in deep sleep in hibernation."

"Truly amazing! how big are the mothers?"

"They weigh anywhere from 90 to 240 pounds! By now, this little thing ought to weigh around five pounds, but she is far from that."

"How do you know that the big bear is the mother?" mama asked.

"I don't know. Maybe she's not the real mother, and the cub's real mother died for some reason. Maybe another mother, who had lost her infant, tried to adopt this one. That would explain why the cub is so thin and weak. She obviously hasn't been fed properly for quite some time."

"You're telling me that the big bear may have adopted the cub?"

Owen the baby hippo with Mzee the old tortoise

"Yeah! You know, it happens more frequently in nature than you might imagine! Elephants are *well known* for adopting babies whose mothers have been killed by poachers. There was a baby hippo that survived the tsunami in Kenya that was adopted by a 130-year-old tortoise. There are cases reported of adult chimpanzees and gorillas adopting orphaned babies. Even big males do it sometimes, not just females."

"Do you think the cub is with a male bear?" asked mama.

"This bear is awfully big, for sure. Perhaps it is a male, but I have no safe way of finding out. Animals know instinctively the sex of other animals, but we do not. Of course, a male wouldn't have any milk. It would certainly explain why the cub is so emaciated."

"What do you think is going to happen to the cub?" mama said.

"If we are lucky enough to get nutrition into her on a regular basis, then I think she may make it. A lot depends on whether the big bear will continue to let me feed her."

"What I really meant is, what do you think the long-term future will be for the cub?"

"Ah, well, that's a different story. I suppose I should call the Fish and Wildlife Service tomorrow and tell them about the cub and the adult bear," dada replied.

"But, what would they do?" mama asked in concern.

"They'd probably come with a team of people carrying tranquilizer darts, and they would use them to anesthetize the big bear. Then they would take the two of them away in separate cages." Molly began to quake all over on hearing dada's words.

"What would become of the two of them?" mama said with mounting distress.

"The cub would probably be sent to a zoo or a sanctuary. My guess would be, the big bear would be released somewhere up north, in the Catskills or the Adirondack Mountains. It could not be around here. Our area of the Ramapo Mountains is too populated."

Molly could not help but let out a whine as dada continued to paint a sad picture.

"What's wrong, my little Molly? Is she having another nightmare?" mama said softly as she bent beneath the table to rub Molly's ear.

There was a long silence. "That would be awful! the cub and the big bear would be separated, never to see each other again. Maybe you should wait a little longer before making any final decision," mama suggested.

"Okay, okay, you are right."

Molly felt so relieved to hear dada say that. She started to wag her tail uncontrollably, which made a loud tapping noise on the floor. "I think Molly is having another nightmare. I bet she is dreaming about bears," mama whispered.

Chapter Nineteen

Coco Comes to Life

Coco needed no encouragement. The next morning, when dada stooped to present the warm bottle of milk to the little cub, she immediately latched on to the nipple as if it were a magnet. Babou watched closely from the branches above, and everyone could hear his happy grunts in the background. Molly, Rags, and Pups crowded around dada to observe more closely.

"That little bear is so good. She has drunk all her milk this morning," dada said with satisfaction.

He put her down, and to his relief, she poked her black, furry head up above the undergrowth. Pupsie and Rags danced up and down with excitement, and Molly could not help but bark with joy.

For a week or so, dada continued to bottle-feed the cub several times a day and give her an injection of antibiotic. As you can imagine, Coco did not like this at all. She would screw her face up even before the needle touched her skin and whine pitifully. Then one morning, dada said joyfully to mama, "she is ready to have solid food."

"Great!" she replied.

Coco rapidly developed a strong appetite and began to put on weight. As soon as she would hear dada and the three dogs coming, she would rush toward them, grunting with excitement, ready for breakfast. She would plunge her face into the large bowl of oatmeal, maple syrup, honey, and milk that mama had prepared for her. Once she had finished eating, the dogs would stay to play with her or go on little explorations of the surrounding woodlands.

One day, Molly asked Babou if he would take all of them back to the lake where he and she had searched for the coconut palms.

"Yes," he said, all excited. "That would be fun." The three of them took turns riding on Babou's back, snuggled in deeply against Coco, while the other two would run alongside.

When they arrived at the lake, Rags told Coco, "Follow me!" Coco crawled behind her to the edge of the water. She plunged her nose in between the weeds. Each time, a frog jumped and screamed with terror before disappearing with a splash back into the water. Rags had developed a special bond with Coco; she imagined herself as her real mother. Pupsie had followed behind, her ears and tail drooped in dejection. She was beginning to feel a bit left out, seeing Rags give Coco so much attention. Pupsie had always been the puppy of the family and was used to having Rags dote on her all the time. Now things were changing.

"I feel hungry, Molly. Let's leave Coco with Rags and Pups and go to look for berries together."

"Good idea," she said. Babou kneeled down immediately, and Molly jumped on his back.

"Ready, steady, go!" she barked with happiness. And off they set.

Before they reached the berry bushes, Molly stepped down. She was trotting alongside Babou when who should pop out of nowhere but Mr. Fox. He was in the same grumpy, arrogant mood that he had been when Molly had first met him the previous autumn.

Seeing Molly, he said, "I thought princesses had to be carried everywhere in special carriages. I didn't know they were capable of walking and running like the rest of us."

Molly couldn't resist replying, "Have you found any chickens lately?" The fox gazed at her with narrowed eyes, and then stomped off in a huff.

To Babou's disappointment, no berries were to be found. It was still too early in the spring. He was looking carefully at the tree branches all around, hoping to find some juicy maple buds to eat, when they heard the bark of dogs far off in the distance.

"Is that Rags and Pups? It sounds that they are in big trouble," Molly said.

"Jump back and hang on tightly. Let's go fast," Babou called out as he broke into a gallop. Molly dug her claws deep into his neck, determined not to fall. The barking became more intense the closer they got to the lake. *Something terrible must be happening to Coco,* Molly thought.

As they reached the lake, they could see Rags and Pupsie jumping up and down and barking their heads off in terror.

"What's wrong?" Molly shouted out as she jumped down from Babou's back.

"It's Coco—she is somewhere up in this big tree, but we can't see her," Rags responded.

Coco becomes independent

"Why did she climb up?" Molly asked.

"We were having a great time playing among the bushes. Then, she started to climb up this big tree, one branch at a time, until we lost sight of her. We kept telling her not to do that because we knew she wouldn't be able to come down on her own, but she wouldn't listen to us." Pupsie explained.

"She must have panicked," Molly said.

"Coco! Coco, come down!" implored Babou.

Her petrified little face popped out at the top of the tree among the branches.

"Let me bring her down," Babou said. He wrapped his massive arms around the trunk of the tree, and in great, lolloping bounces, he reached the terrified little Coco in no time. She was now sobbing uncontrollably. "Don't be so afraid. I won't let you fall."

When Babou touched the ground, Rags and Pups rushed to Coco. They licked and kissed her face, which was scratched all over by the branches of the tree.

"The crisis is over! Let's go home!" Molly said with relief.

Chapter Twenty

Coco's Behavior

They were making their way back when they all came to a halt. They could hear a distant, drumming sound. "What on earth is that?" Molly asked Babou in alarm.

The Male Spruce Grouse

"That's Mr. Grouse," Babou replied. "If we are quiet, we might be able to sneak up on him."

They followed the sound and tried not to snap twigs or rustle the leaves with their footsteps. Suddenly they all saw a large, grayish bird with red, bold patches above its eyes. He was flapping the tips of his wings together in front of his chest in very rapid motion like a musician beating a drum.

"Why is he doing that?" Molly whispered.

"He is hoping to attract a female who might be far, far away in the forest," Babou said. "He wants to tell her that he is a very brave and handsome young grouse, and that she should come and see for herself."

Molly was amazed. *Is it his understanding of the animals of the forest that makes him a king?* she wondered.

Back at the pond, Rags called out to Coco, "Come and take a look." Coco followed Rags in funny, bouncing jumps, a little like the hops and skips that Babou makes when he is happy. She saw something moving in the water.

"What is that?" she asked.

"That's Mrs. Muskrat," Rags replied.

The muskrats had a burrow inside the roots of the old maple tree by the bridge. They had built many tunnels, or lodges as they are called, for their two generations of young. A family of shrews was renting one of them out.

Mrs. Muskrat

Coco was mesmerized to watch Mrs. Muskrat plunge beneath the water in a loud splash, only to surface again a few minutes later with a bunch of bright green leaves sticking out of her mouth. She was bringing food back to feed her young.

They all stared in fascination, watching the muskrat swim forwards, then backwards in dog-paddle style. "What a spectacular swimmer!" Rags said. *What a show-off!* Molly thought.

Coco kept looking at Mrs. Muskrat more and more intensely. All of a sudden, she threw herself into the water and disappeared beneath the surface.

"Where is she? Where did she go?" Rags called out in panic.

For several seconds, they could not see a single ripple on the water until Coco reappeared, her head draped in a tangle of green duckweed.

They could not believe their eyes. Although Coco was a natural-born swimmer, she was gulping water. She coughed and spluttered repeatedly as she tried desperately to catch her breath. She swam in small circles and became more and more panic-stricken.

Pupsie could wait no longer. She jumped headlong into the water in one huge splash. It took her only a few strokes before she was able to get to Coco and, coming up from behind, she nudged her forcefully toward the bank of the pond. Coco crawled out, splashing ice-cold water over everybody, much to Molly's displeasure. She had uncontrollable shivers, and her tiny white teeth chattered hard against each other.

Coco's first swim

Rags rushed toward her, and Babou gently picked her up in his teeth by the scruff of her neck and cuddled her between his paws, trying to warm her up.

Pupsie shook herself energetically from side to side to try to get rid of as much water as she could while Rags licked her all over.

"Pups, you were so brave to go and rescue Coco!" she told her.

Coco sensed that Babou was not pleased with her at all. *Did I do anything bad?* she wondered.

The three dogs said goodnight to Babou and Coco, crossed the bridge, and slowly made their way home. They got halfway up the stairs when they heard a soft, whining sound coming from behind them. They turned to look. Flabbergasted, they stared at each other in disbelief. It was Coco! She had followed them and was about to climb the veranda stairs. Babou was standing on the bridge in utter dismay, stamping his feet up and down and rubbing the sides of his head with his huge paws, obviously unable to make up his mind what best to do.

"Rags and Pups," Molly called out. "Take Coco back to Babou immediately, before mama and dada discover what is going on!"

Rags yodeled with excitement and rushed down the stairs, with Pups close behind. They ran half circles around Coco like collie dogs rounding up sheep. Coco thought this was a new fun game they were playing.

They managed to lead her little by little to a desperate Babou, who was still standing on the bridge. She rushed to Babou, wrapped her arms around his tummy, and gave him a big, fat kiss. From her command post on the balcony, Molly proclaimed, "Well done, Rags and Pups!"

For the first time in her life, Molly wished she could laugh like a human being!

Chapter Twenty-One

Babou's Decision

Coco ran to greet Rags and Pups as soon as she heard them galloping over the bridge.

"Come see what I've found," she bubbled with excitement, as she beckoned them with her paw to follow her. With the claws of her front paws, she furiously dug away the earth, exposing a big, fat, wriggling worm that she gobbled down in one quick go.

"Yum, yum! That was so good!" she said, rubbing her tummy in circles with her paw like Babou did when he ate berries. She got another one and offered it to Rags.

"Thank you, Coco, but I just had breakfast and I would not be able to eat another bite." Rags and Pupsie looked at each other, their stomachs churning in revolt. Coco had finally developed a gourmet taste for maggots and bugs. She had discovered that they lived in the wet earth beneath the lichen-covered stones that dotted the banks of the pond.

Coco looking for frogs

At the edge of the water, among the sprouting wild iris leaves, a couple of frogs were playing what seemed to be the frogs' version of jump rope. They were hopping over each other, back and forth, side to side. Coco wanted to show Rags that she could catch them, but each time she made a grab, they escaped her in gigantic splashes of water and let out desperate screams of fright.

Trotting happily over the bridge, Molly arrived. Babou was waiting for her. He rubbed the side of his head with his huge, flat paw, a sure sign that he had something on his mind.

"What is the matter, Babou?" Molly asked.

"I have many concerns about Coco. We cannot forget what happened yesterday, when she followed the three of you. She is bound to try again."

"I know, Babou, but tell me, what is your biggest concern?"

Babou paused for a while before he said, "Unlike you and your sisters, she must be taught to fear human beings, not to immediately see them as friends."

"I never thought of that, Babou."

She and her sisters loved mama and dada, and they never had to fear human beings.

"Coco has a trusting nature," Babou continued. "It's understandable when you think about it. Your dada helped her when she was very sick and saved her life. Rags and Pupsie looked after her, and you and your dada brought food that your mama prepared for her every day. She was bound to develop a trust and love for all of you. But not all people are going to be like your mama and dada, and not all dogs would be friendly toward young bear cubs."

"How can you teach her not to be so trusting?"

"Coco has to learn what it means to be a bear, Molly."

"What do you mean"?

"She has to understand why bears, like many other wild animals, have to change their habitats according to the seasons and find a winter den where they can hibernate. She has to learn how to search for food and look after cubs in preparation for the day when she will have a family of her own."

"How is she going to learn all that?"

"She will learn all of these things if she becomes part of a bear family now, while she is still young. I have to keep reminding myself, Molly, that I am not Coco's mama."

Molly's heart almost stopped beating. "You mean you will have to leave and take her with you?"

"Yes, Molly, I will."

"When?"

"As soon as possible."

"Why so soon, Babou?"

"Mama bears who still have young cubs would be more likely to adopt Coco."

Molly thought about what dada had told mama that night when she listened from under the kitchen table. She recalled how the "Fish and Game" people would capture Babou, put him in a cage, and then take him far, far away north to release him. They might also send Coco to a zoo or a sanctuary. Molly could not bear the thought of that.

"Human beings cannot decide Coco's fate, even if they have the kindest intentions at heart. You must do that for her sake," Molly said.

Babou was amazed: Molly understood him.

"Where would you go?" she asked.

"Up north, Molly, to the big mountains where my winter den is."

"When will you leave?"

Looking up at the sky, he softly said, "There will be no moon tonight, nor for the next several nights, Molly. It would be safer for us to travel under the cover of darkness and rest hidden during the day."

"Tonight, Babou, tonight?" Molly repeated in shock.

"Yes, Molly."

Molly tried to overcome her sadness.

"How am I ever going to tell Rags and Pupsie that you and Coco will be leaving tonight? They will be devastated."

"I know, Molly," Babou said. "Coco will miss playing with them so much. She is too young to understand the reasons why this has to be, so I am not going to tell her."

"Dada and mama are going to wonder what has happened to you and Coco. I would never be able to explain any of this to them. Imagine, they don't even know what your names are, or that you are a male bear, Babou!"

Chapter Twenty-Two

Into the Twilight

Molly was lying behind her palm tree in a somber mood.

"You seem very down, Molly. What's up?" Pups and Rags asked.

"I have something sad to tell you."

"What?"

"Babou has decided that he and Coco have to leave us." The dogs were in shock; the points of their ears stood instantly, and their tails drooped between their legs. Pups looked deep into Rags' eyes to make sure that she had not misunderstood what Molly had said.

"Is it because Coco is getting naughty?" Pupsie whined.

"No, she is not being naughty. She is just a little cub who wants to explore the forest like a big, grown-up bear."

"So, why do they have to leave?

"Because it is too dangerous for them to stay here any longer. The forest is being cut down a bit more each day and replaced by houses and developments. People will be scared to have bears living in their backyards, and some of them would hunt them like they do the deer."

They all remember too well hearing guns being fired during the hunting season and dada stopping them from running free through the woods.

"There is also another reason," Molly added.

"Which reason?"

"Babou wants to take Coco to a vast forest in the mountains up north. He hopes to find a mama bear with cubs around Coco's age who will adopt her into her family."

"He would leave Coco with another bear?" Rags said in amazement.

"Yes, because that is the only way she is going to learn the many different ways of the wild; only a mama bear can teach her that."

"Why does she need to learn all those things?"

"So that she can survive," Molly said.

There was a long silence before Molly continued. "You see, mama and dada provide us with everything we need. Coco and Babou are wild animals. They must provide for their own needs."

Rags and Pups looked totally devastated and lost.

"When are they going to leave?" Rags finally asked.

"They will start their journey when the moon hides and only a few stars twinkle in the vast, black sky. They will have to go tonight."

For quite a while, Rags and Pups did not respond. Then, they walked toward Molly and both licked her back. She wagged her tail softly, realizing they were together, sharing the same sorrow.

That evening, to mama and dada's surprise, Molly, Rags, and Pupsie did not finish their dinners, but clawed at the balcony door to be let out. The sun, hidden behind the clouds all day long, suddenly flamed above the pond. Dusk was descending.

With a loud flap of wings, a pair of mallard ducks flew up from the pond as they heard the paws of the three dogs crossing the bridge.

By the time the dogs arrived, Babou was already standing upright beneath his old oak tree. Looking a little lost, Coco sat between his feet.

A deep quietness had descended over them all. Rags stepped forward slowly and licked Coco's face all over. "I love you, my little Coco. Be good!"

"I love you too, my little Coco," Pupsie whimpered softly, as she placed her paw on Coco's head and pressed it up and down.

Babou stooped low and Molly gently nudged Coco to climb high up onto his back. "Hang on tightly. You've got a long way to go."

"Where are we going? Coco asked Molly.

"You will see, my little one."

"Molly—" Babou said.

"Don't say anything," she interjected, looking deeply into his eyes.

She was fearful of the dangers that could befall them on their epic journey, but deep in her heart, she knew she would see them again. Trying to be brave, she whispered in his ear, "Ready, steady, go!"

Babou stood up, gave one of his funny little bounces in the air, turned, and disappeared with Coco into the twilight.

Acknowledgments

Our thanks to the staff at Author House, especially Tim Fitch for keeping the files organized, Adam Tinsley for his flexibility and cheerfulness. We also want to thank Reymond Mendez for the artistic lay out of the book and Brian Brown for enthusiastic promotion advice.

We are extremely grateful to Esther Hershenhorn for her endless encouragement, support and guidance during the development of the story.

Our deepest gratitude to Gosha Karpowicz who put her talent and soul into creating artistic paintings for the front cover and inside the book, capturing the spirit of each animal.

We are indebted to all the animals who crossed our path, opening a window on their world and inspiring us to write this story.

Photo Credits

CPSIA information can be obtained at www.ICGtesting.com
Printed in the USA
LVOW01s1516291014

411092LV00006B/20/P